A New Take on ABCs!

S is for Smiling Sunrise

An Alphabet Book of Goodness, Beauty, and Wonder

A gift for

Sahil and Neel

With love from

Vick Wadhwa

For
Simrin, Preetaman,
and all children and
their caregivers

At least ten percent of net earnings
from this book will be given to
health and education projects
for disadvantaged children

For more information, please visit
www.wordsbright.com

A New Take on ABCs!

S is for Smiling Sunrise

An Alphabet Book of Goodness, Beauty, and Wonder

Vick Wadhwa

WORDS BRIGHT
Dedicated to Learning

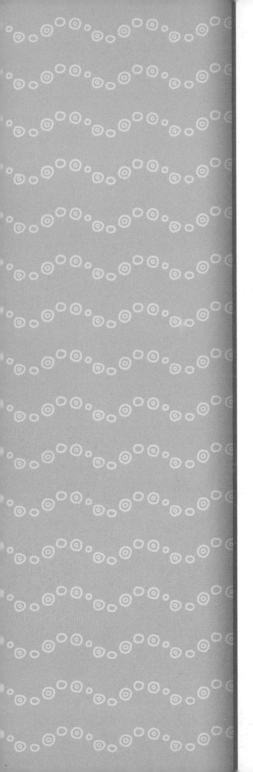

WORDSBRIGHT
Dedicated to Learning

For permissions, bulk orders, or other queries, please send email to:
contactus@wordsbright.com

Images and illustrations by various artists (via www.bigstockphoto.com)
Book design by Peri-Poloni Gabriel (www.knockoutbooks.com)
Published by WordsBright, Newbury Park, CA 91320 (www.wordsbright.com)

Publisher's Cataloging-in-Publication Data

Wadhwa, Vick Manpreet Singh.
    A new take on ABCs – S is for smiling sunrise : an alphabet book of goodness, beauty, and wonder / Vick Wadhwa.
        p. cm.

    ISBN: 978-1-940229-12-6 (hardcover)
    ISBN: 978-1-940229-11-9 (e-book)

Audience: Ages 3 and up (Preschool and up)

Summary: Educational sing-along rhymes, accompanied with an illustrated object or concept for each letter of the alphabet, designed to help children expand their vocabulary and learn positive concepts.

    1. English language—Alphabet—Juvenile literature. 2. Alphabet books—Juvenile literature. 3. Alphabet rhymes. 4. Vocabulary—Juvenile literature. 5. Children's poetry, American.
    I. Wadhwa, Vick. II. Title.
    PE1155 .W23 2014
    428.1—dc23

Library of Congress Control Number: 2013947091

First Edition, 2014

10 9 8 7 6 5 4 3 2 1

Printed in USA using responsibly sourced paper, sustainable soy-based inks, and materials that comply with the U.S. Consumer Product Safety Improvement Act.

A   Artwork   a

A is for Artwork
Drawing and painting
Singing and dancing too
Art makes life interesting!

B Butterflies b

B is for Butterflies

Flying in a flutter
Did you Know, that their wings
Are soft like butter?

Colors

C is for Colors
Speaking words of light
Red and blue, green and yellow
Pink and black and white!

D   Day   d

D is for Dawn and Day
That we get up to
Every day is something new
So always say "Thank you!"

E Evening e

E is for Evening
It's time to sit together
Sun is setting outside
It's time for dinner!

F f

Flowers

F is for Flowers

Fragrant and beautiful
Look and pause, be here now
Be happy and peaceful!

G   g

Gift

G is for a Gift
That you love to get
Did you know, it's as much fun
To give a gift instead?

H  Heart h

H is for your Heart
Lub-a-dub-a-dub
Touch your chest, feel it chug
And give your heart a hug!

I   Infant   i

I is for Infant

Sleeping peacefully
Potential for greatness
Resting gracefully!

Jewelry

J   j

J is for Jewelry

Gems and metals fine

Dreams and goals are inner jewels

When heart and mind align!

K Kaleidoscope k

K is for Kaleidoscope
Brilliant shapes and colors
Twist the tube, see them turn
Triangles to flowers!

L l

Leaves

L is for Leaves so green
Waving in the breeze
Did you know they're making food?
Working with such ease!

M

Moon

m

M is for Merry Moon

Glowing love all night
Bedtime's here, oh my dear
Sweet dreams and sleep tight!

N   Nature

N is for Nature
Forest, hill and river
Sun and clouds, rain and snow
Winter, spring and summer!

O

Ocean

O is for Ocean

Home for fish to stay

Deep and wide, miles and miles

For dolphins to play!

P   Park   p

P is for Park and Playground
Places to have fun
Sit and watch, or go walk
Hop, skip, jump, or run!

Q

q

Quiet

Q is for Quiet times

When we stop talking
Listen close and you can hear
Birds and bugs chirping!

R

Rainbow

R is for Rainbow

Shining in the sky
Look, such lovely colors
Curving far and high!

S s

Sunrise

S is for Smiling Sunrise

Warming up the day
Out of bed, get up quick
Get ready and let's play!

T t

Tasty

T is for Tasty, healthy
Breakfast, lunch, and dinner
"Food is yummy," says my tummy
"And drink plenty of water!"

U Universe u

U is for Universe
Sun and moon and stars
Earth and planets, spinning comets
Galaxies so far!

V V

Virtues

V is for Virtues

Goodness in your heart
Caring, sharing, and honesty
Learn well and be smart!

W W **Words**

oneness

goodness   *beauty*   **wonder**

caring   sharing   HONESTY

LISTENING   **learning**   *BEING*

vision   **effort**   PATIENCE

gratitude

W is for Words we use
Built from A-B-Cs
Know your words, listen deep
And learn through life with ease!

eXcellence

X is for eXcellence

Aiming for the sky
Reaching within, for your best
Growing deep and high!

Yacht

Y is for Yellow Yacht

Sailing through the seas
Gliding on the water
Moving with the breeze!

Z Zebras Z

Z is for Zesty Zebras
Painted black and white
Oh what fun, when they run
The stripes go left and right!

ABCDEFGHIJKLMNOPQRSTUVWXYZ

Now we know that life is beautiful
When we look to see...
Okay dear, let's start over
Let's sing A to Z!

Thank you for buying or giving this book!

Get a free mp3 sound track of the rhymes at:
www.wordsbright.com

About the Book

This book has been carefully designed with four goals: to teach and reinforce the alphabet to young learners; to increase their vocabulary and comprehension by engaging learning and music skills through colorful illustrations and sing-along text; to support character development by conveying a variety of positive words and concepts; and most importantly, to be simply enjoyed!

The rhymes in the book are easily memorized, and fun to sing to the tune of the ABC song. The first rhyme is sung to the tune of letters A to P, the second rhyme is sung to the tune of Q to Z, and then the same pattern repeats with every two rhymes — do give it a try! For more tips about using the book and the rhymes, or to provide feedback, please visit www.wordsbright.com. The website also has information on discounts for bulk orders.

About the Author

Vick is an entrepreneur and scientist, with a Ph.D. in pharmaceutical chemistry. One day, inspired by his toddler daughter, and thoroughly bored with her alphabet books, he set out to write some rhymes that would be fun and educational for her, and motivational for himself. One thing led to another, and *"A New Take on ABCs – S is for Smiling Sunrise"* is his first book. He lives in Southern California, and likes wearing sunny glasses, particularly his invisible ones!

WORDS BRIGHT
Dedicated to Learning